The Big Sticky Bun

Vivian French

Illustrated by
Selina Young

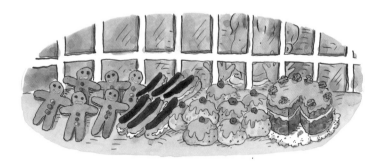

Orion
Children's Books

For Cross Ash Primary School.
Thank you for a lovely visit.

The stories from *The Big Sticky Bun* originally appeared in
The Story House first published in Great Britain in 2004
by Orion Children's Books
This edition first published in 2012
by Orion Children's Books
a division of the Orion Publishing Group Ltd
Orion House
5 Upper St Martin's Lane
London WC2H 9EA
An Hachette UK Company

Text copyright © Vivian French 2004 and 2012
Illustrations copyright © Selina Young 2004
Designed by Louise Millar

The right of Vivian French and Selina Youngto be identified as the
author and illustratorrespectively of this work has been asserted.

The Orion Publishing Group's policy is to use papers that
are natural, renewable and recyclable products and made
from wood grown in sustainable forests. The logging and manu-
facturing processes are expected to conform to the environmental
regulations of the country of origin.

A catalogue record for this book is available
from the British Library

Printed and bound in China

ISBN 978 1 4440 0516 5

Contents

The Big Sticky Bun

"Is Mum back yet?" asked Jason.

"Not yet," said Granny Annie.

Jason sighed. "I'm hungry."

"I'm hungry too!" said Daisy B.

"We'll have tea as soon as
your mum gets home,"
Granny Annie told them.

Jason sighed again.
"Will she be long?"

Granny Annie sat down.
"Why don't I tell you
a story while we wait?"

"What sort of story?" Jason asked.

Daisy B wriggled on to Granny Annie's lap. "Tell us a story!"

Granny Annie nodded. "What sort of story would you like?"

"A story about me!" Jason said.

Daisy B frowned. "No. Me!"

Granny Annie laughed. "I'll start with a story about Jason when he was little. Then I'll tell you a story about both of you."

"Good," said Jason, and he sat down beside Granny Annie. "That sounds fun."

Jason's Big Sticky Bun

Jason was out shopping with his step-dad, Julius.

They'd been to the paper shop.

They'd been to the post office.

"Right," said Julius, looking at his list. "We'll go to the library next. Then the fish shop. Then the supermarket."

"Can I have a big sticky bun?"
Jason asked as they walked past
the cake shop on their way
to the library.

"No," said Julius. "Not today.
We'll get some apples when we
go to the supermarket. Apples are
much better for your teeth."

"Apples are boring," said Jason. "I'd rather have a bun." He began to kick an old can along the pavement.

"Don't do that," said Julius.

Jason kicked the can into the gutter. "Why can't I have a bun?"

Julius sighed. "They're not good for your teeth. And if you have a bun now, then you won't eat your dinner."

"I will," said Jason. "If I promise to eat every little bit of my dinner, can I have a sticky bun?"

"No!" Julius said.

"Please, please, please can I have a bun?" Jason gave Julius a big smile.

"Listen, Jason." Julius sounded cross. "Boys who nag don't get buns."

"What sort of boys do get them?" Jason asked.

"Helpful ones," said Julius. "Boys who help carry bags. Boys who don't kick cans along the pavement. Boys who don't argue."

"OK," said Jason, and he nodded.

Jason was very quiet as he
followed Julius up
the steps into
the library.

When Julius handed in the old
books, Jason said,

"Excuse me, Julius. Shall I look
after the bags while you choose
the new books?"

Julius looked surprised. "What? Oh, yes. That would be great."

Jason sat very still while Julius chose books for Jason's brothers and sisters.

"Are you feeling OK?" Julius asked.

"Yes, thank you," said Jason. "And I don't need to choose a book, thank you. I'm still reading my book on dinosaurs. Thank you."

When they came out of the
fish shop, Jason took the bag.
He carried it all the way to the
supermarket.

He didn't ask for anything
to eat all the way round the
supermarket.

He helped Julius pack the bags,
and then asked which ones he
should carry.

"Jason," said Julius as they walked towards the car park, "you've been a real help today."

"Yes," said Jason. "I know. NOW can we go to the baker's for a big sticky bun?"

Julius nearly dropped his bags. "What did you say?"

"Well," said Jason, "I asked you who got buns. You said boys who were helpful. You said boys who carried bags. You said boys who didn't kick cans. You said boys who don't argue. I've done all that, haven't I?"

Julius groaned. "OK, Jason. You win. We'll get a big sticky bun on the way home. You'd better eat every little bit of your dinner, though."

"Yes," said Jason. He grinned. "I'll eat an apple too."

Daisy B frowned at Jason. "You were naughty! You played a trick on Julius!"

"I wasn't naughty," said Jason. "I was clever!"

Granny Annie smiled. "Yes," she said, "but sometimes you were too clever."

"Was I?" Jason looked surprised. "How can you be too clever?"

Daisy B looked hopeful. "Tell us about Jason being too clever!"

"Well ..." said Granny Annie.

"Please!" said Daisy B. Granny Annie gave Daisy B a hug, and nodded at Jason. "I know just the story. It's about Daisy B too."

"Hurrah!" said Daisy B.

Daisy B and the Football

Jason was out in the garden, playing football. Daisy B wanted to play football too.

"You're too little," Jason said.

Daisy B frowned. "Not little."

"You are," said Jason. He kicked the football towards his sister.

Daisy B tried to stop it, but she couldn't. She ran after it, and tried to kick it – and she fell over.

"Told you," said Jason.

"Waaaaaaah!" Daisy B began
to cry.

Mum was watering the flowers. She came to see why Daisy B was crying.

"She's too small to play football," Jason told her.

"Daisy B," Mum said, "come and help me water the flowers."

Daisy B nodded, and she went
with Mum to fetch the green
watering can.

Jason went with them.

"Why do flowers have to have
water?" he asked.

"Flowers need water to make
them grow," Mum told him.

"Oh," said Jason, and he went
back to playing football.

Mum finished watering the
flowers and went into the house.

Daisy B was still watching Jason.

"Can Daisy B play too?" she asked. "Please?"

"You're too little," Jason said.

Daisy B stamped her foot. "I'm not little! Daisy B is big!"

Jason sighed. "But you can't kick the ball like I can!" He kicked the ball as hard as he could.

It flew in the air, then landed with a crash!! on the green watering can.

"Oops," said Jason, and he ran
to look. The watering can was still
half full of water.

Jason looked at the watering
can, and he looked at Daisy B.

What had Mum said? "Flowers
need water to make them grow."

Jason looked at Daisy B again
... and he had an idea.

"Shall I make you grow,
Daisy B?" he asked.

Daisy B smiled her biggest
smile.
"Yes!" she said.
"Make Daisy B grow!"

"Here we go, then," said Jason, and he poured water all over Daisy B.

"Waaaaaaaaaaaaaaa!"

Daisy B was wet from top to toe. She went running into the house.

A moment later Mum came running out.

"Jason!" she said. "Whatever have you been doing?"

"Daisy B wanted to play with me," Jason explained.

"She wanted to play football, but she's too little."

"She wanted to grow, so I
watered her. Has she started
growing yet?"

"Did I really do that?" Jason asked.

Granny Annie nodded. "Yes! Don't you remember?"

Jason shook his head. "It must have been ᗩges ago."

"Well," said Granny Annie, "it was quite a long time ago. It was last summer."

"I was little then," Daisy B said. "Now I'm a big girl."

Jason began to laugh. "See?" he said. "It worked! You grew!"

Granny Annie was laughing too.

"What else did I do?" Jason wanted to know.

Granny Annie went on laughing. "There was the time when you helped your big brother Ross wash the car ..."

"Tell us!" Daisy B said. "**Please** tell us!"

Jason's Good Idea

The car wouldn't start.

"Oh dear!" said Mum. "I need to go shopping this afternoon!"

"I'll have a look at it at lunchtime" said Julius. "Poor old car. Nobody ever looks after it."

"It's very dirty," said Jason.

"Hey!" said Ross. "I'll clean it!"

"OK," said Julius. "But don't let Jason get wet."

"I'll just watch," said Jason.

Ross began cleaning the car.

Jason stood and watched.

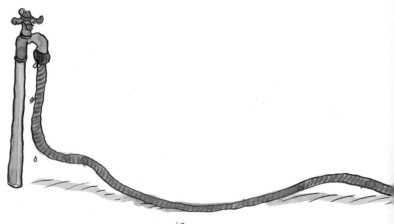

"I can help you," he said. "I like cleaning cars."

Ross shook his head. "No," he said. "You'll get too wet."

"I won't," said Jason.

"Go away," said Ross.

Jason didn't go away. He watched Ross pour water over the bonnet.

Swoosh!

He watched Ross washing the bonnet with a sponge.

Swish, swish, swish! Drip! Drip! Drip!

Jason sighed. He loved playing with water.

"Can I help a little bit?" he asked. "I promise I won't get wet."

"You will," said Ross. "Go away."

Jason didn't go away. He went on watching.

He watched Ross pour water
over the wheels.

Splash!

He watched Ross scrubbing.

Scrub, scrub, scrub.

"Oh no!" said Ross.

"What's the matter?" asked Jason.

"The wheels are really dirty," Ross said. "I need a scrubbing brush."

"I'll get it!" said Jason.

"OK," said Ross. "Thanks."

Jason rushed into the house.

"Mum!" he said. "Ross wants a scrubbing brush!"

"It's in the bathroom," said Mum.

Jason dashed upstairs. The scrubbing brush was on the edge of the bath.

Jason grabbed it, and then he stopped. He looked at the rows of bottles and pots on the bathroom shelf.

"Cleaning stuff!" he said, and he took down a pink bottle.

Jason gave Ross the scrubbing brush.

"Thanks," said Ross.

"I've got some cleaning stuff too," said Jason.

"Great," said Ross. "Pour it in the bucket."

Jason took the top off the bottle and poured.

There was a wonderful smell of roses.

"Smells nice," said Ross. "Thanks, Jason."

Jason smiled. "I'm helpful, aren't I?" he asked.

"Yes," said Ross.

"So can I have just a little go with the sponge?" Jason asked. "If I promise I won't get wet?"

Ross sighed. "OK. Just a wipe or two."

Jason put the sponge into the bucket, and squeezed.

Bubbles burst out – lots and lots of shining bubbles.

"Hey!" said Ross. "What's going on?"

Jason squeezed the sponge on
the car. Bubbles flew everywhere.
"Yippee!" said Jason, and he
squeezed the sponge again.
Bubbly foam flew in all directions.

"Stop it!" said Ross, but Jason couldn't stop. It was too much fun. He squeezed and he squeezed and he squeezed.

There were bubbles in his hair and on his clothes.

There were hundreds of bubbles all over the car. There were thousands of bubbles floating in the air.

"Catch them!" shouted Jason, and he jumped to catch a bubble.

Crash! The bucket fell over with a crash and a splash.

"Jason!" yelled Ross. "I'm soaking!"

Mum came running out of the house. "What's going on?" she said. "Jason – you're wet! And just look at the car! And Ross – you're wet too – oh!"

Mum stopped, and stared at the pink bottle lying on the ground.

"My rose bath oil!" she said. "You naughty boys!"

"It's only cleaning stuff," said Jason.

"That," said Mum, "is my very special, very wonderful rose bubble bath that Gran gave me for my birthday." She sounded very cross indeed.

"Oh," said Jason.
"Sorry," said Ross.

Jason looked at the car.
The bubbles had dripped away,
and the car was shining in the
sunshine.

"Wow!" he said. "I bet our car feels special if it's got very wonderful rose bubble bath all over it. I bet it'll start now!"

"I bet it won't," said Mum, but it did. It started first time, and it smelled of roses for a whole week.

Jason grinned at Grannie Annie. "I remember that," he said. "I had to save up my pocket money to buy Mum more bubble bath!"

Daisy B jumped off Granny Annie's knee. "I can hear someone coming!"

Jason ran to look out of the window. "Yes! Mum's back! She's got loads of shopping."

"Let's put the kettle on," Granny Annie said. "

Jason wasn't listening. "Mum's waving," he said. "Oh!"

"What is it?" Grannie Annie asked.

"She's been to the baker's,"
Jason said. "I can see the bag.
Do you think she's bought buns?"

Jason was quite right. Mum had
bought a bag full of big, sticky
buns ... and they had one each for
their tea.